For Alexandra

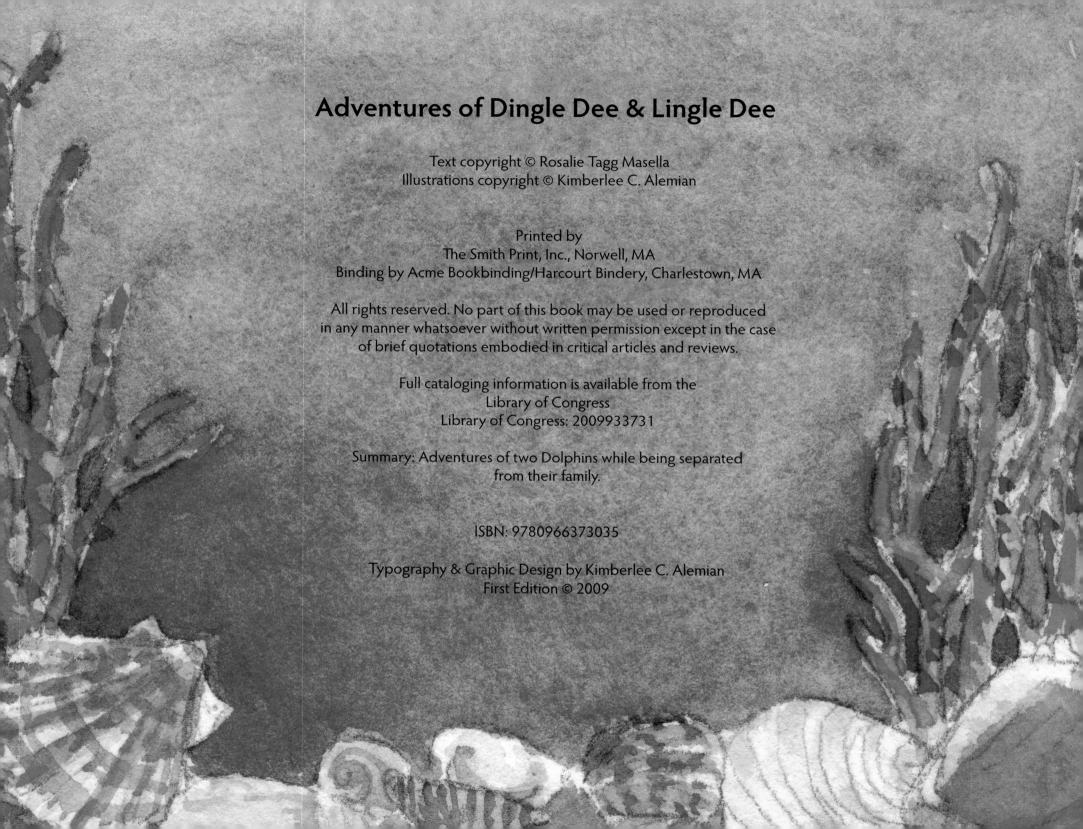

Adventures of Dingle Dee & Lingle Dee

Printed by
The Smith Print, Inc., Norwell, MA
Binding by Acme Bookbinding/Harcourt Bindery, Charlestown, MA

Full cataloging information is available from the
Library of Congress
Library of Congress: 2009933731

Summary: Adventures of two Dolphins while being separated
from their family.

ISBN: 9780966373035

Typography & Graphic Design by Kimberlee C. Alemian
First Edition © 2009

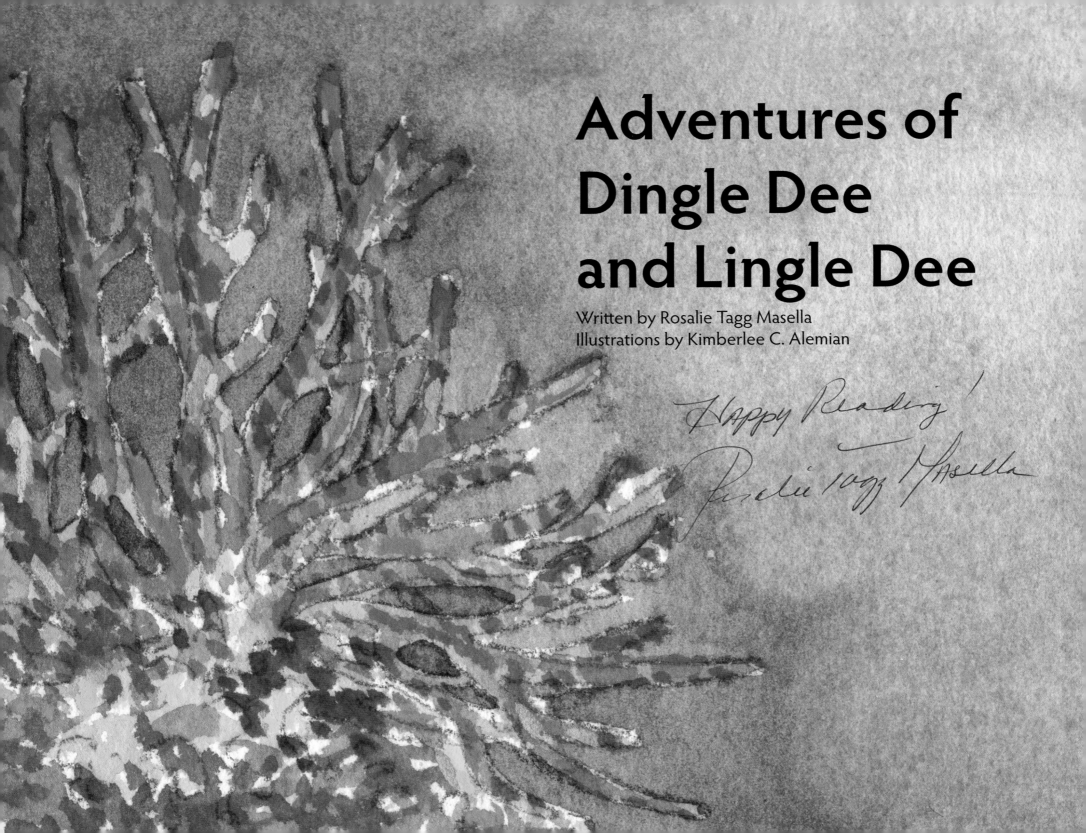

Adventures of Dingle Dee and Lingle Dee

Written by Rosalie Tagg Masella

Illustrations by Kimberlee C. Alemian

Happy Reading!

Rosalie Tagg Masella

Hello my friend, welcome to my undersea world. My name is Dingle Dee. I'm a young bottlenose dolphin. I have a family with brothers, sisters and lots of cousins. My favorite cousin is Lingle Dee. We have lots of fun.

We dolphins have a blowhole on the top of our heads that lets us breathe air in and blow air out. Our blowhole closes when we dive underwater.

One day, our whole family went swimming. Lingle Dee and I stayed in the back of the pod. We kept clicking and whistling to each other about all of the fish we were seeing above and below us. By golly, we were having a terrific time!

We swam, ate and did flips. Lingle Dee and I were swimming slower and slower and slower. When we looked ahead and around us, all we saw were little fish. We didn't see our bottle-nose dolphin family anywhere.

We looked and looked, clicked and clicked. Even with very good eyesight and very good hearing, we still didn't see or hear our bottlenose dolphin family anywhere.

Lingle Dee and I made more clicking and whistling sounds hoping that echolocation, sound waves, would help us find our bottlenose dolphin family, but no clicking sounds bounced back to us.

I clicked to Lingle Dee that we'd better swim faster to try to catch up with our family. Lingle Dee clicked back, "O.K. Dingle Dee." As we were passing a coral reef, we saw a green moray eel. His mouth was moving up and down. This is the way he takes in oxygen from the water. It was daytime and he was sleepy. Moray eels swim the ocean at night.

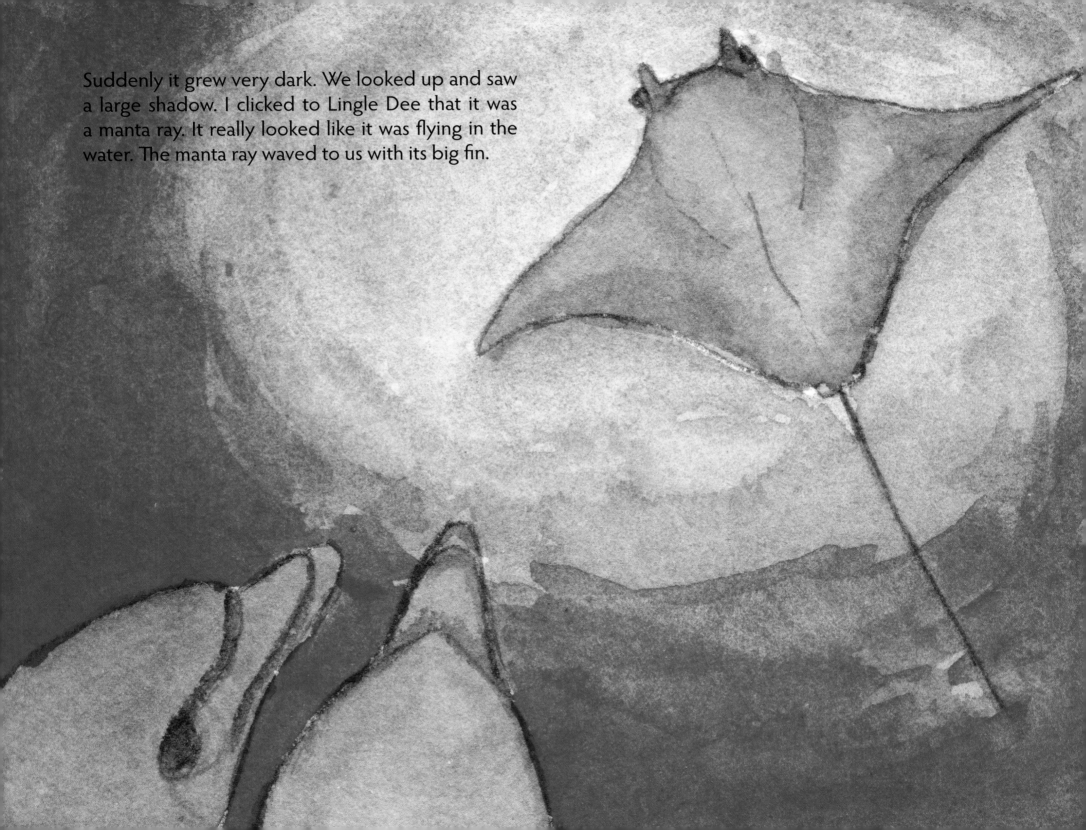

Suddenly it grew very dark. We looked up and saw a large shadow. I clicked to Lingle Dee that it was a manta ray. It really looked like it was flying in the water. The manta ray waved to us with its big fin.

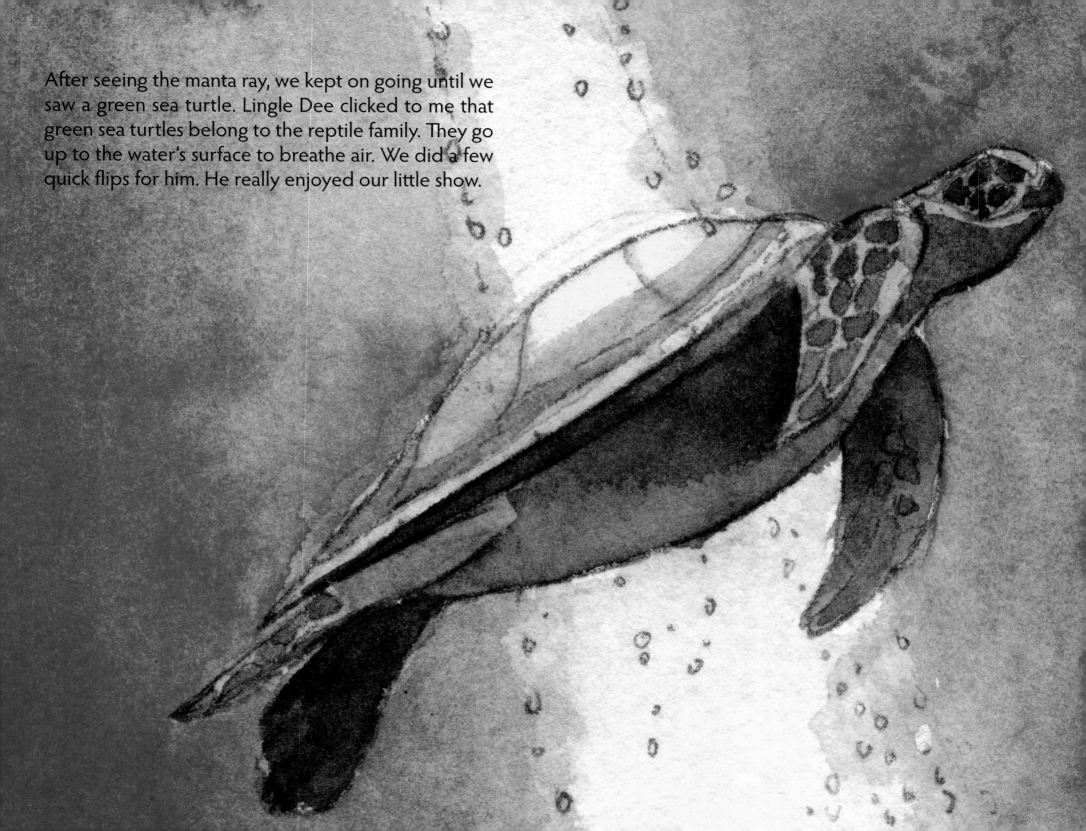

After seeing the manta ray, we kept on going until we saw a green sea turtle. Lingle Dee clicked to me that green sea turtles belong to the reptile family. They go up to the water's surface to breathe air. We did a few quick flips for him. He really enjoyed our little show.

As we were swimming along, Lingle Dee and I spotted a school of barracuda. Barracudas have really sharp teeth. We clicked to each other that we had better move on, quickly.

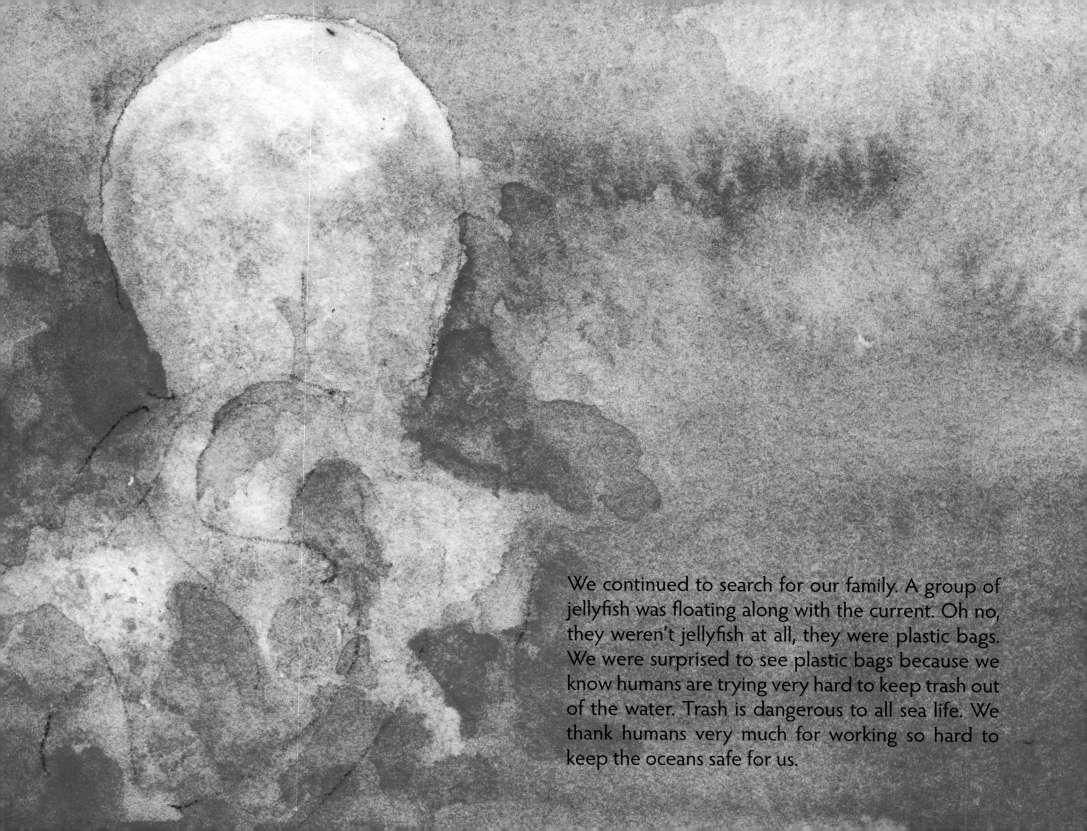

We continued to search for our family. A group of jellyfish was floating along with the current. Oh no, they weren't jellyfish at all, they were plastic bags. We were surprised to see plastic bags because we know humans are trying very hard to keep trash out of the water. Trash is dangerous to all sea life. We thank humans very much for working so hard to keep the oceans safe for us.

Off we swam closer to the beach, still hoping to find our bottlenose dolphin family. Humans wearing bathing suits were shuffling their feet as they walked into the ocean. They shuffle to scare away stingrays that might be hiding in the sand. Stingrays don't mean to hurt humans but they do have a sharp barb at the base of their tail. If accidentally stepped on, this barb could hurt a person.

After swimming by the beach and not seeing our family, Lingle Dee and I clicked that we should head out into deeper water. Open ocean was ahead of us. We were becoming very tired, hungry and lonely for our family.

On our way to open ocean, we came upon two pretty angelfish. They had electric blue bodies and yellow tails. Angelfish are very shy and usually travel in pairs. We both waved a flipper to them as they quietly swam away.

Oh my! A big bull shark came very close and frightened us. Our bottlenose dolphin family warned us to be very cautious with bull sharks. We sped up using our strong dolphin kick, then dove deeper and farther away from the bull shark.

The big bull shark didn't follow us. We wondered why.
Just then we heard lots of familiar clicks and whistles.
It was our bottlenose dolphin family! They chased the
bull shark away from us.

Our family circled around us. They clicked that they had been worried about us all day and were so happy to find us safe and sound. We joined our dolphin family pod. Together we swam back into familiar home waters.

Happy to be back, we all had a delicious dinner. After dinner, Lingle Dee and I did double high flips with our family. What a nice pod of bottlenose dolphins Lingle Dee and I have!